Yoga Threads

Musings of a Western Yogini

Jean Grant-Sutton

Original Artwork by Marjorie Richardson and Celia Mayo

Editing by Zahira Rabinowitz

Design by Deborah Perdue, Illumination Graphics

DEDICATION

My students have inspired me to keep teaching
by their enthusiasm, devotion, and choice to join
with me on the inner journey.
I dedicate this to them as my teachers!

Also to my family and friends who give me the ground
to practice.

And to the masters who have guided my way.

PREFACE

This is a compilation of snippets from my stack of notes from classes I have taught in the past 20 years.

And even a few that were written in my early 20s while I was on my year-long adventure to Southeast Asia, India, Nepal, and Sri Lanka.

If any of you remember the small book called *Notes to Myself* by Hugh Prather, it is like that.

I'm aware, and have been since I was young, that I have a personal, constant open line of communication with the Creator. So do you, by the way :) I have been responsive to the information that flows through me as a sentient being and recognize what asks to be transmitted to my students through my guidance.

I am grateful, so incredibly grateful, to have been able to share with my students a way to enliven and encounter a connection to body, breath, mind, emotions and spirit. Both the individual feeling within and the larger sense of it. As One.

I hope that these small bites will be easily assimilated and digested and will bring nourishment to your soul and whomever you share them with.

For me, yoga is an essential tool for survival in our overwhelming outer world and find that it expands the creativity and joy in my life.

I wish that for you as well.

May we cherish this life journey and continue to grow our unity consciousness.

Jean Grant-Sutton

Yoga is a remembrance and felt experience of unity.

Through conscious breath, gentle movement, and
positive thought, we intentionally bring peace and
contentment to our feeling experience.
We turn our attention to our inner state. As we
connect with our internal self, our mind can become
reflective and we can choose to respond with caring and
understanding rather than with reactivity
and defensiveness.

We learn from yoga to mindfully balance effort and ease,
which supports developing a harmonious state of mind
that helps us cope with life's challenges.

Yoga provides a lens of wholeness to help us understand how to navigate life's hardships and blessings.

As we take time to feel into, study, and experience the play of opposites we are able to embrace wholeness and peace.

Yoga practice supports direct experience of the silent

shimmering life force that suffuses all things.

Success in yoga poses is not about how perfectly we do them, but how present and responsive we are while we are in them.

Yoga involves a sensing, feeling, in-the-moment alertness rather than ambitious striving or believing that more is better.

The point of practicing asanas (poses) is to become sensitive, attuned, and adaptable as we experience a sense of integration.

Yoga is considered by many to be a mental discipline
geared toward understanding the expansion of
consciousness. I agree.

I've grown to understand, quite clearly, that what I put
my attention on is what I experience.

Our body is a laboratory for self-exploration.

I am thankful for my ability to open my perception to blending the miraculous with the mundane.

Practicing deep breathing and mindful movement invokes a relaxation response, which soothes our nervous system.

As we feel into our body's intelligence we connect to
the joyful celebration occurring inside.

Yoga is self-care medicine. It calms our physical system
and our mind.

Allowing universal love to flow through me, I can love
freely and without fatigue. My heart becomes a vessel
for healing love.

In the wholeness/oneness perspective is a fundamental acceptance of everything just as it is. This brings peace.

Letting go of controlling how we think things should be makes space for our emotions to fluctuate while we maintain ease and happiness.

Set your lips into a sweet smile and all your feel-good

chemicals will flow.

Take a DOSE: Dopamine, Oxytocin, Serotonin,

Endorphins.

Let your thought of impermanence magnify the
preciousness of each moment.

We can receive spirit into our being like a sponge
receives water.

When we discover the vibrations, oscillations, and flickers of the life energy that animates our being, we understand our body is an instrument of the divine.

Freedom is an attitude of mind that comes when we realize we are not our mind.

Body and mind are tools of consciousness.

Be present as you observe your thoughts, emotions,

and reactions.

When you can sense the wonders of life available to you, you can obtain nourishment from sunshine, fresh air, trees, and nature. This nourishment will also come from your lungs, your in-breath, and your out-breath.

Sense yourself as the conduit for the life force energy

that flows through you.

Time spent on the yoga mat enveloped in mind/
body/spirit sensitivity, breathing, and openness to all
arising sensations, thoughts, and feelings (pleasant
or unpleasant) will support our ability to encounter
difficulty with equanimity in daily life.

Immersing in yoga develops our awareness of and connection to our inner geography. We call this embodied consciousness.

To support the health of your immune system, practice relaxation and stress reduction. This will also facilitate good circulation.

Yoga helps us move through contraction and expansion while simultaneously tuning us to an underlying state of peace and harmony.

Our organs, muscles, and arteries contract during
stress response. In yoga, we release tension, clear stress
chemicals, and increase blood flow
to support relaxation.

To become more conscious of our eternal being we feel
into the invisible energy field that is composed of waves
and particles. Joy comes to the surface as we sense the
molecular dance within us.

There is a background matrix in which everything exists. We become still to support our attunement to it.

Yoga brings homeostasis to the body/mind, which leads to a deeper understanding of our impermanent nature.

We move through the doorway of our physicality

to discover the dimension of inner space.

Keep coming back to presence without strain, without struggle, without self-judgement. Meet it with a friendly attitude that brings a gentle smile to your being.

Life manifests its mysterious unity through its endless diversity and we enter the sacred oneness as we honor the multiplicity.

Reflect rather than react.

Soften rather than harden.

See things now, in the moment, without dwelling

on past or worrying about future.

Bring the mind into the body, focusing your
consciousness throughout—your head, neck, arms,
torso, legs and feet. Notice when you sense full
inhabitation. Send love through the matrix
of your form.

Bring your awareness to the bottoms of your feet, feeling
the solid ground you are on. This will always bring you
home to yourself, wherever you are.

If we did nothing but conscious breathing practice,
we would be refreshing, renewing, and revitalizing our
energy, our organs, and our spirit every day.

Deeper than thought is the vibration of aliveness.

Enjoy that.

We establish harmonious balance as we flow with
the primordial rhythms of creation, preservation,
and dissolution.

Let the moment-to-moment process of sensitivity lead
you to an easeful stillness, feeling your whole being in a
comfortable relationship with ground, gravity,
and space.

Faith is filled with patience, perseverance, endurance,
devotion, and love.

Our perspective shapes our reality.

Happiness is a state of being that can be encouraged through your thinking: thinking of all your blessings with deep appreciation and gratitude.

Feel deeply into the direct experience of the strands

that generate the process of change, transformation,

and evolution.

We continually recreate ourselves through our choices.

＊

We are infused with light in every cell of our being.

＊

Our breath stokes the fire in every cell of our body so we
can shine and radiate amidst the world's darkness.

Taking time to feel yoga allows us to directly experience
the interplay of form and formlessness.

As we become more alert to energy, we can be more
responsible for what we bring into our solitary and
shared space.

Becoming aware of our central energy channel gives us a wonderful guidepost for centering.

The yoga perspective sees life as a dynamic process of learning. We're here to evolve our consciousness to experience our essential nature as Oneness. There is nothing that is not part of the One.

To maintain equanimity don't get distracted by pain
and pleasure; when you do, let go again.

Two key statements to tell yourself:
"Never give up" and "Always let go."

The inner journey helps us to recognize when our primitive fight-or-flight response is triggered so we can quickly pause to choose our response rather than react automatically.

I love the multidimensional perspective we work with.
Physically, we ease tension that builds in our tissues
and stores as agitation. Mentally, we focus the mind so
normal chatter slows and quiets some.
Emotionally, we sense the feeling and positively
influence it through our internal communication
network. Energetically, we support the vibrancy of our
cells with conscious breathing. Spiritually, we awaken
to the divine energy that streams through us and
everything, everywhere, always.

We all go through times when the light is eclipsed by the
darkness of uncertainty, unknowing, or loss.

It is possible to soften our hearts and feel love
and goodness amidst all the suffering we hear and
experience daily.

◎

We discover we are not our thoughts; we can observe
them flitting here and there and then tap into the
eternal light of consciousness itself.

◎

At a deep level we are learning to instruct our brain to
soak our neural network in positivity, goodness, beauty,
and love.

As we heighten our sensitivity to this moment we attune to the aliveness of being. It feels good.

Feel and allow vastness to flow through you.

I find yoga to be an essential tool not only for survival

but for expanding creativity and joy in my life.

The science of yoga was developed to help us realize

peace and joy can be found within ourselves.

One of the things that has kept me enamored with yoga over the years is the time it allows me to grow my relationship to spirit.

Treat the body as a temple. Nourish it, pamper it, actively love it.

Broadcast love wherever you go; pour out a blessing to all beings, to all life on planet Earth.

We practice with focused determination yet release attachment to any specific outcome.

You are a luminous, buoyant, radiant work of art at the layer of your sparkling, light-filled bones.

When you notice you are having a beneficial experience, take time to let it soak into your neurons.

I experience yoga as an experiment in the laboratory of the human body and wholeness as the content of our consciousness.

Aligning our thoughts, words, and actions with truth creates harmony.

Make it a priority to listen for the yes or no

from the body.

Yoga is an exceptional system for becoming aware

not only of the body but also of the life force

that animates it.

As humans we have a super power coming from our cerebral cortex—it is the power of choice.

Yoga is a tool for health and healing.

Steady, deep breathing with long exhales activates our parasympathetic nervous system, which is where our relaxation response is located.

We are made of stardust—a combination of mainly

carbon, hydrogen, oxygen, and nitrogen.

We are spinning with the earth and our galaxy

and expanding with the universe.

It takes time, patience, and practice to cultivate a clear,

open heart/mind.

Within that open heart/mind we can rest in radiance,

bliss, and unity.

An aspect of the stress response in our bodies (fight, flight, or freeze) is contraction around the skeletal muscles. This reduces circulation and promotes accumulation of toxic residue that results in inflammation, pain, and movement restriction. Long slow exhalations can break the grip as we consciously communicate relaxation to our muscles.

Consciously cultivating loving-kindness, friendliness,
and goodwill in our heart/mind acts as an antidote to
hatred, fear, and aversion.

As we watch the leaves fall we can appreciate the
tenderness and beauty of our temporary existence.

Cultivate your discernment to see if your thoughts are contributing to well-being. If not, use your power of choice to make it so.

Give yourself space for transformation to occur. Breathe, find where you feel resistance, and let it go.

Yoga is a high-level stress management tool.

We originate from light as does all life via
photosynthesis. We can sense into the light-conducive
molecules within our cells and illuminate
the joy of living.

A whole palate of feelings flow through us—not all positive: sadness, anger, annoyance, frustration, fear, etc. We can allow them to arise and pass more freely by invoking a friendly self-compassion and self-acceptance.

Cultivating conscious presence is a pathway to awaken
the radiance within.

Slowing down and savoring the moment reduces fatigue
and improves our energy level.

Yoga practice asks us to make a continued effort, when we have negative thoughts, to reflect on the opposite— to reframe to the positive.

I am a multi-dimensional being. I abide in a magical structure that connects all parts to keep balance and the flow of well-being.

Tidbits from 1981 and 1982
on Year Long Trip:

Peace is in every moment, therefore be aware of
every moment.

Unfolding destiny splashes hope on a dried out spirit.

Pain is in the fragmentation; beauty is in the whole.

The important things of life are not purchased; they are
seen, felt and heard.

Move—beyond ego toward love, beyond judgement
toward acceptance, beyond struggle toward ease.

Embracing the moment fully will connect you to a deep
love. You will feel a yearning and the intensity
of being alive!

During intervals of emptiness between times of
movement and flow, changes take hold; old patterns go.

Learn to free the mind from the tentacles of opinion and
judgment and flow with the shades
of thought and feeling.

Subscribe to your inner magazine that publishes nothing
but the truth.

Acknowledgments

I've had the amazing fortune to have had access to so many amazing Wisdom and Yoga Teachers over the years. When I read my snippets or teach my classes, I can hear the echos of the influencers of my time.

I was always open in myself to learn as much as I could from the teachers who touched something in me. Whether it was a physical, energetic, psycho-emotional, or spiritual awareness, I always felt the resonance of their teaching within me.

And I've included my family and students who have helped guide my way.

Thanks deeply to:

My mother, Beverly Grant(my first teacher)

My father, James Eugene Grant(my first teacher)

My sisters who support me always,
Teresa Grant and Deborah Perdue

My loving husband, Nicholas Sutton, who has been
instrumental in keeping me in my studies all these years
and is my rock.

My loving daughter, Nicole Mitchell, who both grows
me and loves me with her bright, beautiful heart.

My loving son, Spencer Sutton, who soaks up the
teachings with such sensitivity and intelligence and
speaks my language.

Sri Aurobindo and the Mother

Kate Pelly (my beloved mother-in-law)

BKS Iyengar

Ian Rawlinson

TKV Desikachar

Joseph Le Page

Anodea Judith

Richard Miller

And most recently, Dr. Ananda Baliyogi Bhavanani

And to:

Rodney Yee

Judith Lasater

Mary Paffard

Erich Schiffman

Scott Blossom

Jon Kabat-Zinn

Anne O'Brien

Stephen Cope

Richard Freeman

Deepak Chopra

Pema Chodron

Neale Donald Walsh

Thich Nhat Hanh

Jack Kornfield

John Records

Eckhart Tolle

Mark Nepo

Michael Beckwith

Dr. Steve Hadland

Baxter Bell

And to all my amazing students who have contributed
to my growth for so many years, too numerous to
mention here.

9 798869 309723